Creative Keyboard Presents THE DISCO

An Introduction to Boogie, Rock, Blues, & Jazz

For Easy Piano

by Robert Benedict

The CREATIVE KEYBOARD DISCOVERY SERIES is a contemporary collection of volumes which invites the student to explore the realms of classical music, folk, jazz, blues, boogie, rock, etc. Each book provides easy to intermediate arrangements designed to capture and sustain musical interest while guiding the student through the varied styles of repertoire.

It is Robert Benedict's belief that a student's commitment to an instrument and the development of technique can best be inspired by providing good arrangements of the type of music the student loves most. "Student repertoire must be interesting. Music has changed greatly in the past 50 years because of electronics, the recording industry, communications, new types of instruments, etc. There is now a strong swing by piano teachers to encourage and teach the various new styles of music, new left-hand accompaniment techniques, improvisation, popular music, etc.; and a background of classical training can be expanded upon in many ways. I believe that the degree to which the student is able to manage the varied styles of repertoire is indeed a fine reflection on the student, the teacher, and the teacher's choice of music."

Foreword

This book has been compiled to introduce students to popular music. I have covered various modern piano styles – boogie woogie, rock 'n' roll, blues and jazz, as well as some gospel and folk. This repertoire has been combined with study notes and some tips on modern harmony; this will clarify and organize in the student's mind and fingers, the various popular styles. I have illustrated the music using simple key areas, primarily C major. Aspiring students will transpose the repertoire and musical concepts to other keys.

Robert Benedict

Contents

Simple Rock

Introducing the chords C, F, and G.

Chords

Here's how to build the C, F and G chords used in "Simple Rock":

Chords are built from scales.

For the C major chord, combine the first, third, and fifth notes from the C major scale.

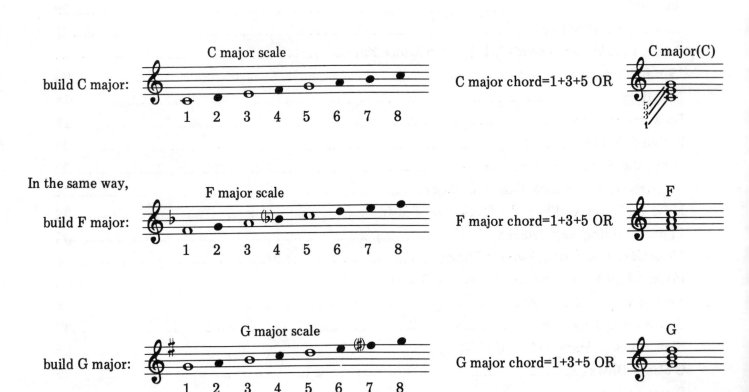

These are the three most common chords in the key of C, and are the basis of boogie woogie, rock, blues, and jazz. They are called the primary chords.

Here is the same chord progression - this time with a new rhythm.

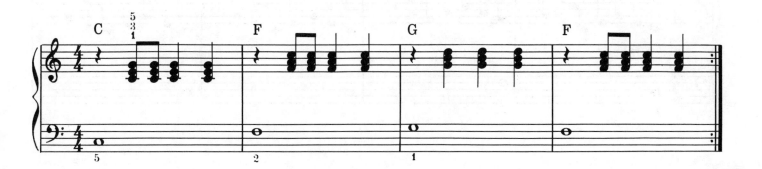

.✦ The Harmonized C Scale *✦.✦*

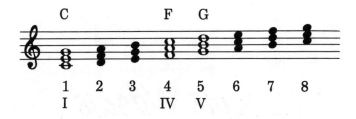

The bottom notes form the C major scale.

We have built chords on every note of the scale, above.

It is common to use Roman numerals to identify each chord in the scale:
I II III IV V VI VII (VIII=I)

Here, we have identified the three primary chords only:

     I = C
   IV = F
    V = G

8-Bar Rock

* tonic chord: the chord whose name is the same as the key.

Boogie Woogie

Introducing the flat seventh note.

In the boogie woogie style, the flat seventh gives a characteristic feel to the music.

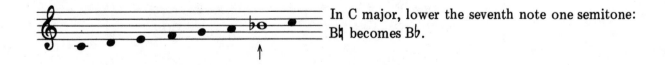

In C major, lower the seventh note one semitone: B♮ becomes B♭.

In F major, E becomes E♭.

Boogie In The Right Hand

Here, the left hand plays the chords while the right hand plays a very common 12-bar sequence.

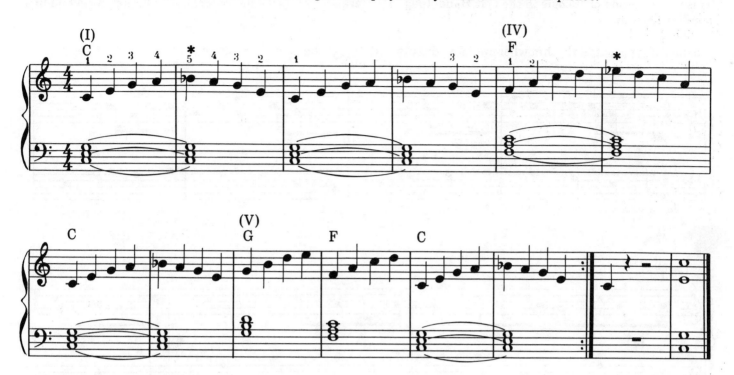

* Listen to how the flat 7th is used with each of the chords:
  In the C chord, B♭ is used.
  In the F chord, E♭ is used.
  Each chord has a distinct blues feel when this scale interval is added.

Boogie In The Left Hand

More with the flat 7th.

Here, the left hand plays the boogie melody.

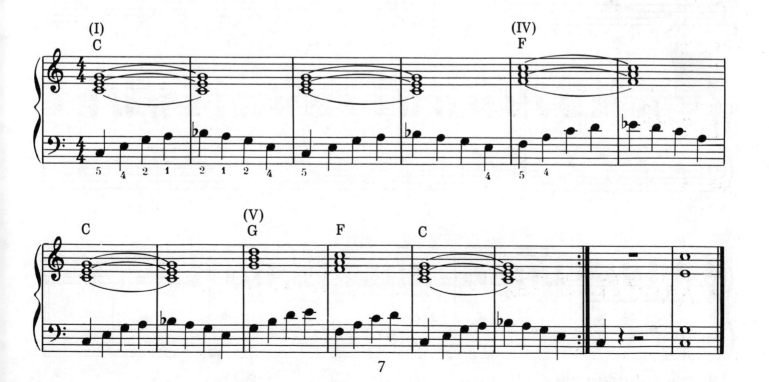

7

Syncopated Boogie

This is a variation of "Boogie in the Left Hand" (page 7). Here we use the same chords, but in broken form and in a familiar rhythm.

We have a <u>syncopated</u> rhythm when we have accents that are <u>off</u> the beat.   > =accent

Boogie in C Major
Flat 7th.

Different inversions of the right hand chords are used, but the chord progression is the same.

* staccato (short, detached)

Piano Boogie

You can substitute this rhythmic variation in the left hand as well.

Note: The variation can be used in every second bar:

etc.

Country Rock

In this piece, both hands work together to create a steady rock rhythm.

Here is the rhythm, written out in one line:
Tap it, using both hands, before you play.

Try to bring out the moving part in the left hand with the thumb and index finger.

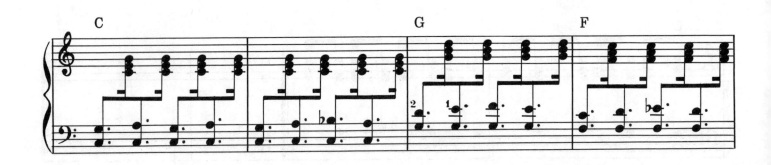

Note: If you relax this rhythm, it becomes ♩ ♪ ♩ ♪ , a "shuffle".

10

.· More About Chords *.·*

Here, we introduce the II chord (D minor) in the key of C, as well as the III chord (E minor).

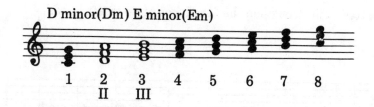

Both of these triads are <u>minor</u>. (The interval between the root and third above is a <u>minor</u> third.) Listen to the sad and melancholy sound characteristic of the minor triad. Compare it with the brighter, happier major triads I, IV, and V studied previously (page 5).

.· Michael, Row The Boat Ashore *.·*

Using the II and III chords.

*Note: C/E = C Major chord with an 'E' bass.
   G/D = G major chord with a 'D' bass.

Arr. by R. Benedict

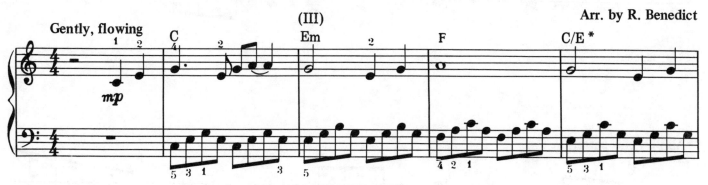

8-Bar Boogie

With chords I, II and V; introducing alternating octaves.

Here is a left hand boogie pattern which is very popular and effective. In "8-Bar Boogie" we are using this pattern in C major, with chords I=C, II=Dm and V=G.

Watch the accents. This pattern will strengthen the 5th finger of your left hand.

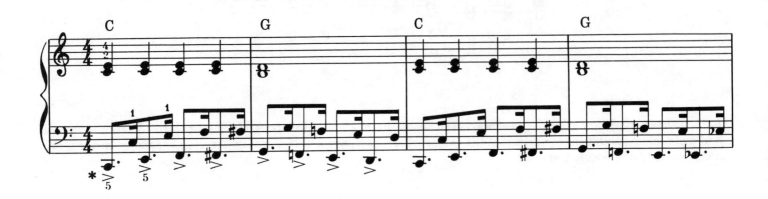

* > =accent

Also try this pattern:

Cockles and Mussels
A Jazz Waltz

Here, we introduce another minor triad, the VI chord (A minor) in the key of C:

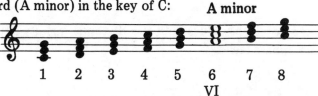

Note that all of the minor chords, Dm, Em and Am are often altered to become Dm7, Em7 and Am7. Add the seventh note above the root. This added seventh creates a jazz or popular feel in an arrangement:

Dm7 = DFA+C
Em7 = EGB+D
Am7 = ACE+G
Also, G7 = GBD+F (the G major chord with the added Seventh).

"Cockles and Mussels" is a very old Irish folk song and has been arranged here with a "jazz waltz" accompaniment. Tap the steady $\frac{3}{4}$ rhythm with your foot while you play the syncopated rhythm of your left hand. Then add the melody.

Arr. by R. Benedict

13

·*·Bass Boogie·*·
Using chords I, IV, V and II

Here is a type of 12-bar blues with the rhythmic melody alternating from the right to left hand. Play staccato and with a skipping feeling.

chromatic
chord change

Repeated notes are a great exercise, especially for the fifth finger of both right and left hands.

REVIEW
Here are the chord changes of this familiar progression, so you can easily hear and understand the harmonies used.

COUNT: 1 2 3 4   1 2 3 4

Cmajor   Fmajor   Cmajor   Dminor7 G7   Cmajor

BAR 1   2   3   4   5   6   7   8   9   10   11   12

Amazing Grace

(A Gospel)

Jazz Waltz

CHORD SEQUENCE: Here we use both the tonic chord (C) and C maj7. C maj7 = C major plus the seventh note of the C scale (not the flat 7th). In this progression, the major 7 chord creates a relaxed tonic sound. The fourth chord in the key of C, the F chord, has also become F maj7; again, the seventh note (this time in the scale of F) is added. I have also used Em7, the third chord in the key of C, and as well, the dominant or fifth chord, G7.

Note: F/C = F major chord with a "C" bass.

C/E = C major chord with an "E" bass.

Arr. by R. Benedict

15

Silent Night

With all the diatonic chords.

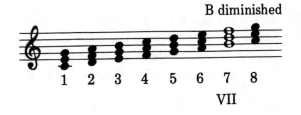

B diminished

1 2 3 4 5 6 7 8

VII

Here, we introduce the last diatonic chord in the key of C, 'B diminished' or B°. It is built on the seventh degree, B♮, and is a diminished triad with two minor 3rds, resulting in a °5 between the outer notes. When the flat 7th is added to this triad, it becomes Bm7♭5.

Bm7♭5

NOTE: This arrangement also brings together <u>all</u> the diatonic chords we have discussed, most with the added seventh.

*This chord is often used in an approach to the relative minor, or VI degree, as in this arrangement.

Arr. by R. Benedict

16

The Battle of Jericho

A gospel, in a blues style.

Arr. by R. Benedict

Discover

A <u>review</u> of the harmonized C scale, with added 7ths.

Play the whole-note triads first, listening carefully to the notes in each chord as you slowly move along.

Then, play the full 4-note chords, and listen to the modern texture of the added sevenths. This harmonized scale is the basis of modern harmony.

17

Dixie Rock

Introducing the diminished 7th chord.

The 4-note, diminished 7th chord is made up of three minor 3rds. It is commonly used between IV and V, as in this arrangement.

F#dim7

R. Benedict

Good Ol' Rock 'N' Roll

Here, we are in the key of G major, but still use the chords I (G chord), IV (C chord) and V (D chord). Look for the flat or "blue" notes in the left hand, i.e. C# being played at the same time as, or "against", C♮ (see bar 12).

R. Benedict

19

.· Chord Progression *·*

The cycle of rising 4ths.

In chord progression, we most often move in rising perfect fourths (because there is a dominant tendency in every chord).

Ex. C → up to F, Dm → to G, G7 → to C etc.

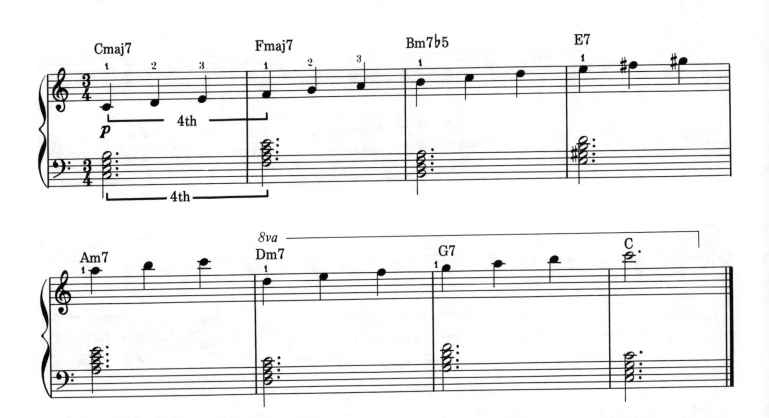

Becoming aware of this natural cycle of rising fourths helps us to generally understand music, improvise, and organize in the mind and ear the natural tendencies of musical progression. This awareness will also help you to memorize music.

Sometimes we use augmented 4ths (diminished 5ths) in the cycle (as in the above example, F maj7 to Bm7b5, not F to Bb) so as to stay in the established key area.

The chords can be major, minor, sevenths, etc.

Look at all of your repertoire and discover how, generally, chord progressions move in rising fourths.

Summer Romance

Introducing the 'sus 4' chord, and the use of rising 4ths

R. Benedict

Here, we have a G major chord but with no 3rd. Instead, we add the "suspended" fourth note, "C". This note usually "resolves" to the 3rd in the next chord.

Boogie Song

Arr. by R. Benedict

Note: The accents fall on different beats, giving this arrangement a real "Swing" feel.

Three Blind Mice Rock

In order to create the feel of a piano boogie, try to play the dotted rhythm ♪. ♪ in a relaxed, triplet style ♩ ♪.

Arr. by R. Benedict

Boogie in A Minor

Introducing I, IV, and V in a minor key.

Arr. by R. Benedict

Here are the primary chords, I, IV, and V, but now in the key of A minor. (We use the harmonic minor-with G#-to build the chords.)

12-Bar Blues in A Minor

This is the standard chord progression for the common "12-bar blues", here in a minor key. It can be summarized as:

Am	Dm	Am	Am		I	IV	I	I
Dm	Dm	Am	Am	or	IV	IV	I	I
Em	Dm	Am	Am		V	IV	I	I

where each symbol corresponds to one bar.

Improvise your own right hand part. Use the "natural" scale of A minor (extended).

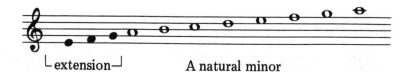

└ extension ┘   A natural minor

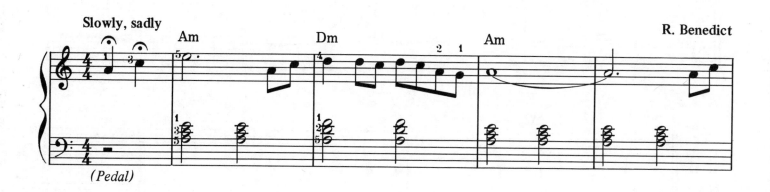

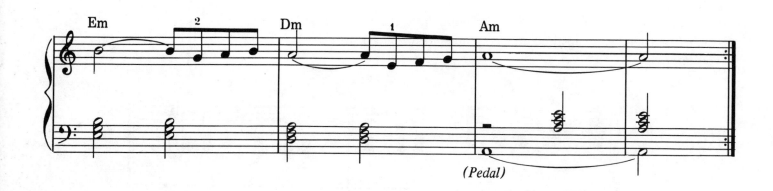

'50's Rock

This progression - C, Am, F, G - I - VI - IV - V - was most popular in the '50's with writers like Buddy Holly, Elvis Presley, and other rock 'n' roll artists of this period.

With spirit

R. Benedict

* Before the "G7" chord in the right hand, the "F" chord is sustained from the previous bar. This is called IV over V, or F/G.

Try substituting Dm for F (II for IV) .

Also, improvise your own melodies with notes from the C major scale. Your teacher or friend can substitute this accompaniment pattern while you improvise.

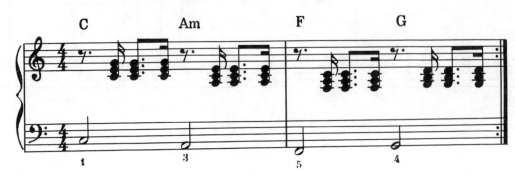

Rock Progressions

Here are some short rock progressions in C, or A minor. You can use these with other musicians as a basis to create your own pop music.

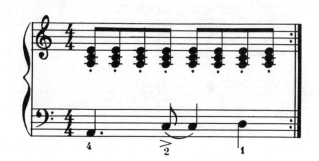

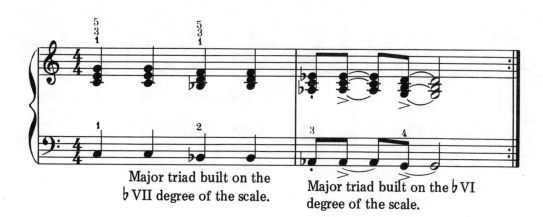

Major triad built on the ♭VII degree of the scale.

Major triad built on the ♭VI degree of the scale.

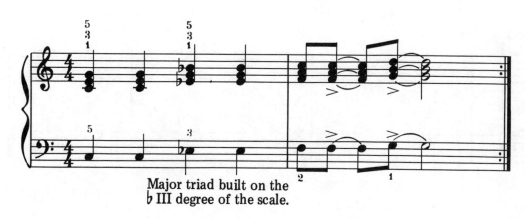

Major triad built on the ♭III degree of the scale.

Bellamy Street

A slow folk rock tune.

Notice that the progression of chords is approximately the same in each line.

R. Benedict

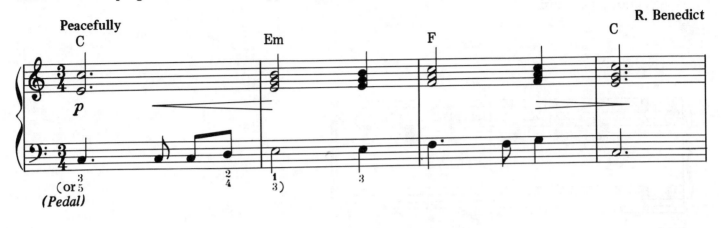

When The Saints Go Marching In

Gospel, in a country blues style.

Arr. by R. Benedict

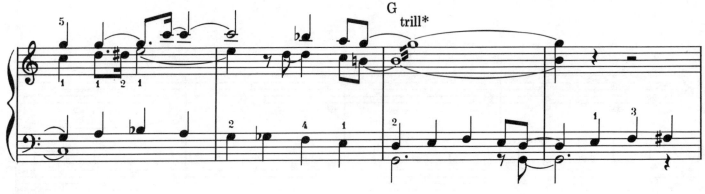

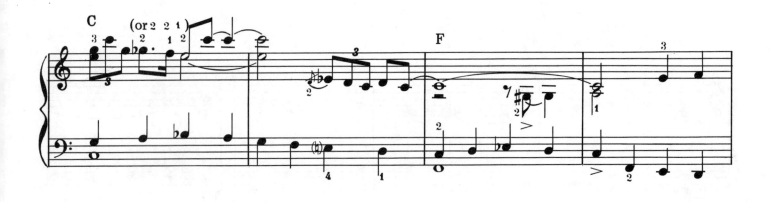

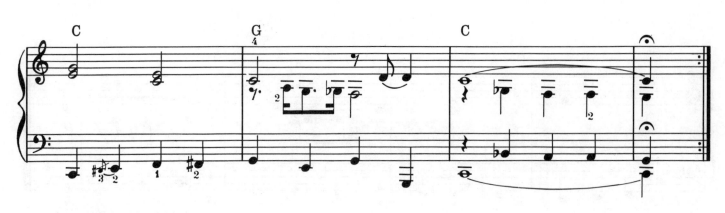

*·*Discover*·*

Resources for Improvisation in C major

Here are some melodic cadences or endings which are very popular. Spend plenty of time with these fragments; you've heard them before, and your musical memory will help you. Later, try them in different keys.

see "When the Saints . . ."
on page 30

major pentatonic scale

minor pentatonic scale

Discover

More Cadences and Popular 'Licks' or 'Fill-ins' for Modern Piano

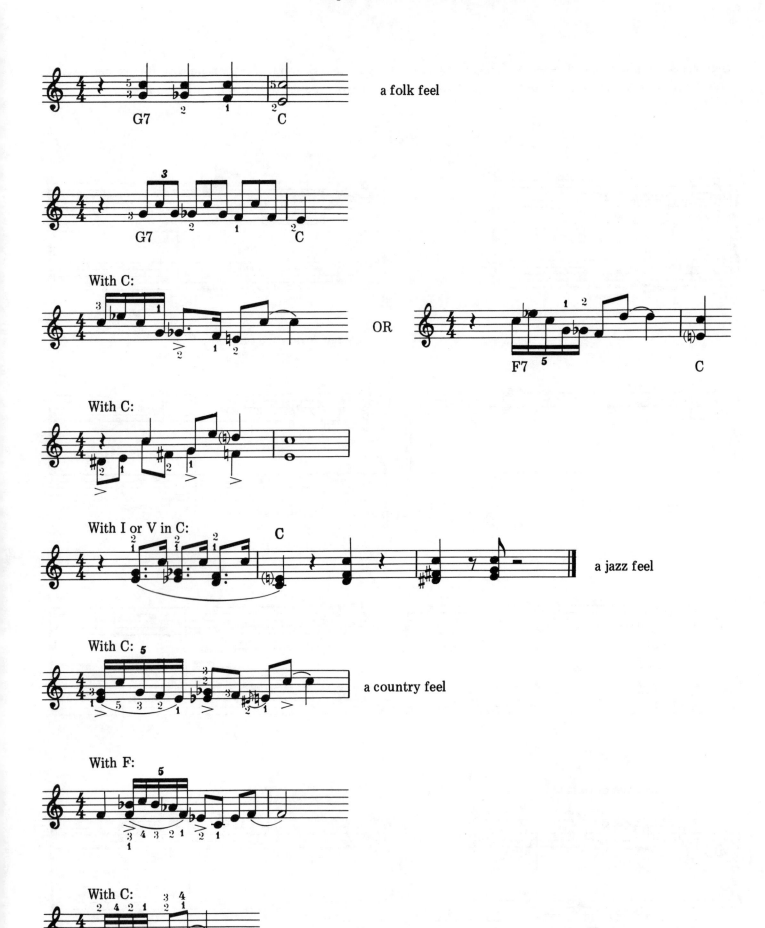

a folk feel

OR

a jazz feel

a country feel

Chord Building Supplement

C major = 1, 3, 5 = C, E, G	C aug = 1, 3, ♯5 = C, E, G♯
C minor = 1, ♭3, 5 = C, E♭, G	C dim = 1, ♭3, ♭5 = C, E♭, G♭
C maj7 = 1, 3, 5, 7 = C, E, G, B	C7 = 1, 3, 5, ♭7 = C, E, G, B♭
Cm7 = 1, ♭3, 5, ♭7 = C, E♭, G, B♭	C6 = 1, 3, 5, 6 = C, E, G, A
Cm6 = 1, ♭3, 5, 6 = C, E♭, G, A	Csus4 = 1, 4, 5 = C, F, G
Cm7♭5 = 1, ♭3, ♭5, ♭7 = C, E♭, G♭, B♭	Cdim7 = 1, ♭3, ♭5, °7 = C, E♭, G♭, B♭♭ (A)
C+9 = 1, 3, 5+9 = C, E, G, D	Cmaj7+9 = 1, 3, 5, 7+9 = C, E, G, B, D

C9 = C7+9 = 1, 3, 5, ♭7+9 = C, E, G, B♭, D

C♭9 = C7+♭9 = 1, 3, 5, ♭7+♭9 = C, E, G, B♭, D♭

Caug9 = C7+aug9 = 1, 3, 5, ♭7+♯9 = C, E, G, B♭, D♯

C13 = C9+13 = 1, 3, (5), ♭7, 9+13 = C, E, (G), B♭, D, A

C♭13 = C9+♭13 = 1, 3, (5), ♭7, 9+♭13 = C, E, (G), B♭, D, A♭

Discover
More cadences using 9ths and 13ths

1) G9 C+9

Variations on V-I (or G-C) in C major:
G9=G7+9
In "G9", the seventh is implied (must be included)

C+9=C triad with the added ninth (no seventh)

2) G♭9 C+9

3) Gaug.9 Cmaj7+9

4) G13 Cmaj7+9

"G13" implies 13th+9th and 7th

5) G♭9♭13 C+9

6) G♭9♭13 C6+9

7) Gaug.9♭13 Cmaj7+9

The augmented 9 above G is A♯, which can be written as B♭ when the melodic line falls, as in:

8) Gaug.9♭13 C+9

9) F(m) C

The IV–I Cadence

In this cadence, the IV chord can be either major or minor.
(i.e. in C major, IV can be F major or F minor)

Here we use the IV minor triad (F minor) over ♭II(D♭), followed by C major.

10) Fm/D♭ C

Here we have a similar IV-I feel, but this time with D♭maj7 (♭II maj7) (instead of F minor) going to C.

11) D♭maj7 C

34

.˙Rockin' Mill Wheel*.*

Using the minor pentatonic scale, the most common scale used in popular music today.

Carefully learn the left hand first, using the fifth finger as a pivot.

R. Benedict

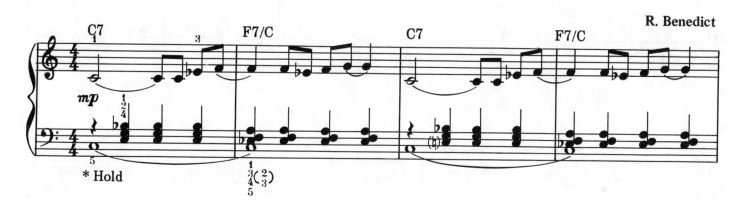

* Hold

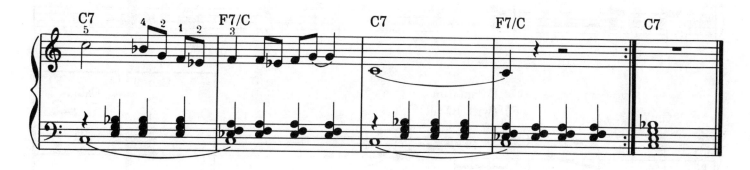

The tied notes in the right hand give the "rock" feel to this little piece. Notice that the left hand chords are major (E♮ in C+) but the melody is minor (uses E♭, the "blue" note).

Improvising the right hand

Once you have learned "Rockin' Mill-Wheel", you can make up your own rock melodies by improvising the right hand. At first, only use the notes taken from the following scale:

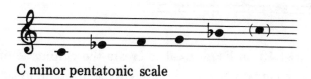

C minor pentatonic scale

Remember: Keep the left hand steady, and simply play any of the C minor scale tones in your own order. Have some fun!

Jazz in F

Work on the left hand first; play it very staccato and count the rests.

R. Benedict

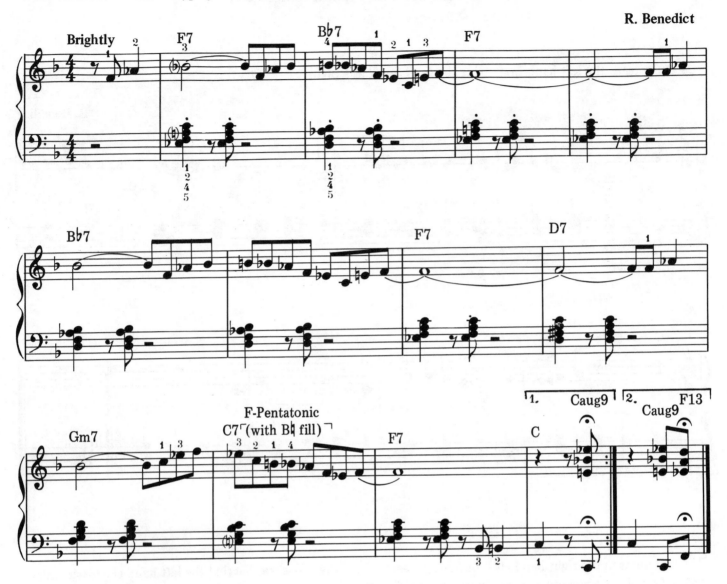

F+ is a common key for jazz, blues, etc.

Here is the pentatonic jazz or blues scale of F minor:

In the above piece, B♮ (augmented 4th in F+) is used to create the chromatic line B♭ - B♮ - C. This interval is a common addition to the blues or pentatonic scale in any key, and is used in jazz, blues, rock, gospel, etc. It broadens the scale and creates melodic tension.

NOTE: Notice that the left hand in bar I plays F7 - with the major third 'A', yet the right hand uses A♭ - the 'blue' note.

IMPROVE YOUR IMPROVISING!   After confidently learning and memorizing the left hand jazz accompaniment, go ahead and improvise the right hand; use notes from the F minor pentatonic scale.

Improvising

Jazz in F

Here are some common right-hand suggestions which should be practised as short exercises, and then used with "Jazz in F" (opposite page).

With any of the chords F7, C7, D7, etc., use:

a)

b)

Keep your improvising light and articulate.

Offbeat accents occur almost constantly in jazz melody. Imagine the regular $\frac{4}{4}$ pulse behind your improvisation; tap your foot to the $\frac{4}{4}$ beat and feel the syncopation.

The Right Hand in Two Parts

The added "name of the chord" note ("F" in the first example) gives a country flair to the jazz improvisation.

Use with the chord F or F7:

With Bb7, transpose to: *etc.*   With C7, transpose to: *etc.*

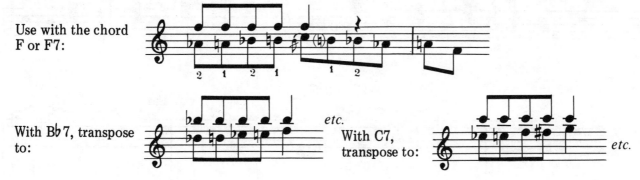

NOTE: A "name of the chord" note can be added above any of your own right-hand improvisations.

With the chord F or F7, use:

Here, we have a trill between the minor 3rd, "C" and "Eb", preceded by a grace note (the grace note is played at the same time as the dotted half "F").

With Bb7, transpose the above to: With C7, transpose to:

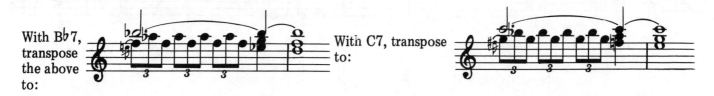

37

Slow Blues

Here are three new chords: ♭II (maj7), ♭III (m7), and ♭VI (7). ♭II (D♭) is often used at a cadence and has a IV-I feel (see page 34).

D♭maj7

♭III(E♭) theoretically becomes a major7 chord (built up from the C natural minor scale):

E♭maj7    but is often used between II and III,

as a chromatic passing chord:

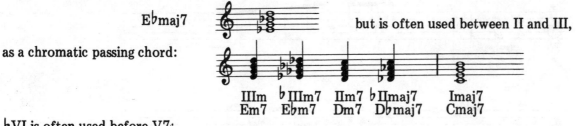

IIIm	♭IIIm7	IIm7	♭IImaj7	Imaj7
Em7	E♭m7	Dm7	D♭maj7	Cmaj7

♭VI is often used before V7:

A♭(maj)7

The title "Slow Blues" is used by musicians to refer to a general style implying a slow progression of the following chords (in any major key).

Note: This piece has been composed with "licks" and "fill-ins" taken from page 32.

R. Benedict

38

C Minor Blues

A <u>minor</u> blues is often played in a flat key.

In this piece, the upper part should be light and staccato.   The flats of the key have been added to simplify reading.

R. Benedict

Above, the left hand plays a standard "walking bass".

<u>Note</u>: Here are 3 ways to improvise in the bass part, using the same right hand:
1. Use the scale tones derived from the chords. Other notes (D♭ in bar 2, F♯ in bar 3) are used to help connect the primary scale tones.
*2. Notes may be repeated (as in bars 1 and 2 *) to create a stronger rhythm. Use <u>very short</u> 16th or grace notes.
3. Octaves can be used in the bass.

i.e.

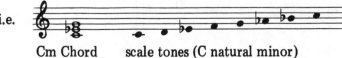

Cm Chord   scale tones (C natural minor)

39

★ ·. Baroque Jazz ·. ★

We often think of extemporization (improvisation) in only modern terms such as jazz, blues, rock, etc. Actually, improvisation was much more common a few centuries ago, with spontaneous compositions or "impromptus" in the style of Bach, Beethoven, Mozart, Chopin, etc. Their piano compositions themselves were organized improvisations.

Here is an improvisation which quotes musical fragments taken from very old repertoire including the Christmas carol "Good King Wenceslas", folksongs "Twinkle, Twinkle Little Star" and "Oh, Susanna" as well as the national anthem "O Canada".

Listen to how the melodies stitch through the main fabric of the harmony. They are quoted in various keys and harmonic settings.

Note: Sing the melodies as you play. To perform this piece effectively, try to accentuate the themes so that they are highlighted well above the counterpoint.

R. Benedict

Good King Wen - ces - las looked out on the Feast of

Twin-kle, twin - kle, lit - tle star, how I won - der

Stephen.

what you are.

For I come from Al - a - ba - ma with my____

ban - jo on my knee.   O   Can - a - da,   glori - ous   and

free,   we   stand   on   guard,   we stand on   guard   for   thee.

O Canada

A Duet in Pop Style

Secondo

C. Lavallée
Arr. by R. Benedict

O Canada

A Duet in Pop Style

Primo

C. Lavallée
Arr. by R. Benedict

43

Secondo

Primo

45

Index